Campden
Research As...

Chipping Campden
Gloucestershire
GL55 6LD UK
Tel: +44 (0) 1386 842000
Fax: +44 (0) 1386 842100
www.campden.co.uk

Guideline No. 42

HACCP: A Practical Guide
3rd Edition

Editor: R. Gaze

2003

© CCFRA 2003
ISBN:0 905 942 60 4

Reprinted 2005

Campden & Chorleywood Food Research Association Group comprises

Campden & Chorleywood Food Research Association

and its subsidiary companies:
CCFRA Technology Ltd   CCFRA Group Services Ltd
Campden & Chorleywood Magyarország, Hungary

PREFACE

HACCP is now well established amongst many food manufacturers and processors, especially medium to large-sized companies, as the main preventative approach to assuring food safety. It is also increasingly being adopted by smaller food companies and, at the start of the food supply chain, by farmers and growers. Approaches to HACCP also continue to evolve.

This new edition of CCFRA's long established practical guide to HACCP reflects the developments since the second edition published in 1997. In particular, it describes and explains the idea of 'prerequisite programmes' as an increasingly important part of HACCP and highlights how HACCP has become relevant to a wider range of food businesses. It also takes the opportunity to explain HACCP verification and validation, to draw attention to related developments in microbiological risk assessment, to emphasise the importance of training in the implementation of HACCP and, finally, to illustrate some typical approaches to HACCP documentation.

Robert Gaze
CCFRA

ACKNOWLEDGEMENTS

CCFRA wishes to thank the many members of the industrial working parties and expert reviewers involved in the development of the previous editions of this guide, and also the CCFRA membership as a whole for funding the project under which this guide was revised and updated.

The editor would specifically like to thank the following CCFRA staff for their help: Les Bratt, Alan Campbell, Adam Chappell, Su Leaper and Phil Voysey.

EXECUTIVE SUMMARY

HACCP stands for Hazard Analysis and Critical Control Point. It is a science-based analytical tool that enables management to introduce and maintain a cost-effective, ongoing food safety programme. HACCP involves the systematic assessment of all the many steps involved in a food operation and the identification of those steps which are critical to the safety of the product.

HACCP is applicable to the identification of microbiological, chemical and physical hazards affecting product safety. HACCP should only be applied to food safety, but the technique may, with care, be used to identify and control hazards associated with the future microbial spoilage and quality of products. HACCP must be applied to a specific process/product combination, either to an existing process or as part of a development brief, and will require the full commitment of senior management, production and technical staff to provide the resources necessary for successful analysis and subsequent implementation.

The HACCP approach allows management to concentrate resources on those steps that critically affect product safety. A HACCP study will produce a list of Critical Control Points (CCPs), together with controls, critical limits, monitoring procedures and corrective actions for each CCP. For continuing safety, full records must be kept of each analysis. The efficacy of the study must be verified on a regular basis and the HACCP plan must be reviewed when aspects of the operation or product change, or when new information concerning a foodborne pathogen or other hazard emerges with public health significance.

One of the many advantages of the HACCP concept is that it will enable food manufacturing or catering companies of all sizes to move away from a philosophy of control based primarily on end product testing (i.e. testing for product failure), to a preventative approach whereby potential hazards are identified and controlled in the food processing environment (i.e. prevention of product failure).

HACCP is a logical and cost-effective basis for better decision making with respect to product safety. It provides food processors with greater control over product safety than is possible with traditional end product testing, and when correctly implemented may be used as part of a defence of 'Due Diligence'. HACCP has both national and international recognition as the most cost-effective means of controlling foodborne disease and is promoted as such by the Joint FAO/WHO Codex Alimentarius Commission.

This Guideline describes the principles of HACCP and is also a practical guide for its application. It includes examples of microbiological safety issues, because food contaminated with microbial pathogens is the most common cause of illness but, as mentioned earlier, the principles outlined are also applicable to chemical and physical safety hazards and microbiological spoilage.

CONTENTS

SECTION 1: INTRODUCTION AND HISTORY OF HACCP

1.1   What is HACCP?

HACCP is the acronym for 'Hazard Analysis and Critical Control Point'.

It is a system of food safety assurance based on the prevention of food safety problems and is accepted by international authorities as the most effective means of controlling foodborne diseases. HACCP is derived from 'Failure Mode and Effect Analysis', an engineering system which looks at a product and all its components and manufacturing stages and asks what can go wrong within the total system.

The HACCP system applied to food safety was developed in the 1960's jointly by the Pillsbury Company, the United States Army Laboratories at Natick and the National Aeronautics and Space Administration in their development of foods for the American space programme. It was necessary to design food production processes to ensure the elimination of pathogens and toxins from the foods. As this could not be achieved by finished product testing alone, the HACCP concept was initiated.

In 1971, the Pillsbury Company presented HACCP at the first American National Conference for Food Protection; since then the concept has been evolving in the food industry. The US Food and Drug Administration incorporated HACCP into its Low Acid Canned Foods Regulations (1973) and has applied HACCP to seafood production processes. The US Department of Agriculture has applied HACCP to meat and poultry production. The World Health Organisation (1995, 1996) and International Commission on Microbiological Specifications for Foods (1988) have encouraged the use of HACCP, as has the UK Government following recommendations made in the Richmond Report (1990, 1991) and the Pennington Report (1997). An effective application of the HACCP system may help to demonstrate 'Due Diligence' under the UK Food Safety Act (1990). The Codex Alimentarius Commission promotes practical implementation of HACCP systems in the food industry. The Food Hygiene Committee of Codex has documented a standardised approach to HACCP to be used by all its member countries. This document adopts the Codex "HACCP System and Guidelines for Its Application" 1993 and its revision (1997). Codex standards, guidelines and recommendations have been identified as the baseline for consumer protection under the Agreement on Sanitary and Phytosanitary Measures (1994), agreed at the Uruguay round of GATT negotiations. The work of Codex has become the reference for international food safety. Within Europe, systems based on HACCP principles have been incorporated into the EC directive on the hygiene of foodstuffs (1993) and subsequent legislation. A number of other countries have mandatory requirements for HACCP, particularly for seafoods.

HACCP is a management tool that provides a more structured approach to the control of identified hazards than that achievable by traditional inspection and quality control procedures. It has the potential to identify areas of concern where failure has not yet been experienced and is therefore particularly useful for new operations. By using a HACCP system, control is transferred from end product testing (i.e. testing for failure) into the design and manufacturing of foods (i.e. preventing failure). There will, however, always be a need for some end product testing, particularly for verification purposes.

Much of the effectiveness of HACCP is achieved through the use of a multi-disciplinary team of specialists. The team should have skills from relevant areas, e.g. microbiology, food science, production, quality assurance, food technology and food engineering.

In order to carry out HACCP, the team of specialists follow the seven basic principles which are detailed in Section 2. This approach involves the identification and analysis of potential and realistic hazards associated with all stages of food product manufacturing from raw materials to the consumption of finished products; microbiological, chemical and physical hazards should all be considered if they affect product safety. Following hazard analysis, Critical Control Points (CCPs) are identified with appropriate measures which can be applied to control each hazard. Monitoring procedures for the critical limits at the CCPs are designated with appropriate corrective action plans. Finally verification systems are put in place to ensure that the HACCP is working effectively.

The developing technique of Microbiological Risk Assessment (MRA) (Codex, 1999) and industrial MRA (CCFRA, 2000) may assist in the development and validation of effective HACCP systems. Over recent years, the concept of MRA has gained considerable favour as a means of assessing the degree of risk associated with a particular hazard. The concepts of HACCP and MRA can complement each other very well. HACCP is an operational system designed to deliver safe foods through production. That is, HACCP is a means of managing the control of a particular hazard. MRA is a design tool to help the manager assess how big a risk a particular hazard is; thus, MRA can be used to improve a HACCP system. HACCP is likened to the Risk Management component of Risk Analysis, rather than the Risk Assessment component.

This Technical Manual is designed to assist all companies to develop and maintain effective HACCP systems. It contains recommendations on how to bring together the necessary team and how to carry out HACCP, and practical advice on implementation. Advice on training of individuals concerned is given, along with hints and warnings from experienced HACCP users.

1.2   Benefits

The benefits from the use of HACCP are many and varied. Key benefits may include:

- HACCP is a systematic approach covering all aspects of food production from raw materials, growth, harvesting and purchase to final product use to assure safe food

- Use of HACCP will move a company from a solely retrospective end product testing approach towards a preventative Quality Assurance approach

- HACCP provides for cost-effective control of foodborne hazards

- A correctly applied HACCP study should identify all currently conceivable hazards, including those which can realistically be predicted to occur

- When supported by generic food hygiene control measures, the use of HACCP focuses technical resources into critical parts of the process

- The use of preventative approaches such as HACCP leads to reduced product losses

- HACCP is complementary to other quality management systems

- International authorities such as the Joint FAO/WHO Codex Alimentarius Commission promote HACCP as the system of choice for ensuring food safety

- Implementation of HACCP will be useful in supporting a defence of 'Due Diligence' for UK food safety legislation

- HACCP facilitates international trade

- HACCP complies with legal requirements

1.3   Scope

HACCP is a powerful system which can be applied to a wide range of simple and complex operations and is not restricted to large manufacturers. It is used to assure food safety at all stages of the food chain. For food business operators to implement HACCP they must investigate not only their own product and production methods, but must also apply the principles of HACCP to their raw material supplies and to finished product storage, and must consider, where appropriate, distribution and retail operations up to and including the point of consumption.

The HACCP system may be applied equally to new or existing products. It may be convenient when introducing HACCP to apply it to new products or new production methods or parts of processes. It may also be used to ensure the effectiveness of production support operations such as cleaning systems.

The aim of this document is to outline the principles of HACCP as applied primarily to microbiological food safety and to demonstrate how the principles may be put into practice by giving examples of HACCP studies. These examples include microbiological safety, physical safety and chemical safety hazards in food manufacturing and catering environments.

1.4   HACCP and product quality

The HACCP technique was developed initially to deal with microbiological hazards that affect product safety and also those leading to microbial spoilage. Increasingly it has become accepted that the technique is primarily applicable to issues of product safety associated with biological, chemical or physical hazards.

During recent years, however, there has been increasing interest in the application of the HACCP technique to identify hazards and control measures associated with product quality defects (e.g. particle size, colour, taste, texture). In theory, the philosophy inherent in the HACCP technique (i.e. identify potential hazards and put in place control measures to prevent them occurring) is equally applicable to both product safety and quality issues (including microbiological spoilage). However, there is a significant body of opinion that believes that HACCP should be restricted to product safety issues.

It is essential that the overriding importance of HACCP as an internationally accepted method of assuring the safety of foods is not diluted, or confused by attempts to derive CCPs for such topics as product quality attributes. It is recommended that HACCP is targeted at product safety issues, but where quality issues are included, a clear distinction between safety and quality must be shown.

1.5   Definition of terms

Definition of terms used in this manual:

CONTROL (noun)	The state wherein correct procedures are being followed and criteria are being met.
CONTROL (verb)	To take all necessary action to ensure and maintain compliance with criteria established in the HACCP plan.
CONTROL MEASURE	Any action and/or activity that can be used to prevent or eliminate a food safety hazard or reduce it to an acceptable level. [cf. Preventative Measures NACMCF (1992)].
CORRECTIVE ACTION	Any action to be taken when the results of monitoring at the CCP indicates a loss of control or trend towards loss of control.
CRITICAL CONTROL POINT (CCP)	A step at which control can be applied and is essential to prevent or eliminate a food safety hazard or reduce it to an acceptable level. A step is a point, procedure, operation or stage in the food chain, including raw materials, from primary production to final consumption.
CRITICAL LIMIT	A criterion which separates acceptability from unacceptability.
DECISION TREE	A sequence of questions which can be applied to each process step with an identified hazard to identify which process steps are CCPs.
DEVIATION	Failure to meet a critical limit.
FLOW DIAGRAM	A systematic representation of the sequence of steps or operations used in the production or manufacture of a particular food item.
HACCP	A system which identifies, evaluates, and controls hazards which are significant for food safety.
HACCP PLAN	A document prepared in accordance with the principles of HACCP to ensure control of hazards which are significant for food safety in the segment of the food chain under consideration.
HAZARD	A biological, chemical or physical agent in, or condition of, food with the potential to cause an adverse health effect.

HAZARD ANALYSIS	The process of collecting and evaluating information on hazards and conditions leading to their presence to decide which are significant for food safety and therefore should be addressed in the HACCP plan.
MONITORING	A planned sequence of observations or measurements of CCP control measures. The records of monitoring provide evidence for future use in verification that the CCP is under control.
PREREQUISITE PROGRAMMES	The measures that provide the basic environmental and operating conditions in a food operation that are necessary for the production of safe and wholesome food.
TARGET LEVEL	A predetermined operational value for the control measure which has been shown to eliminate or control a hazard at a CCP (see also TOLERANCE below).
TOLERANCE	The values between the target level and the critical limit.
VALIDATION	Obtaining evidence that the elements of the HACCP plan are effective.
VERIFICATION	The application of methods, procedures, tests and other evaluations, in addition to monitoring, to determine compliance with the HACCP plan.

SECTION 2: HACCP PRINCIPLES

HACCP is a system which identifies specific hazard(s) (i.e. any biological, chemical or physical property that adversely affects the safety of the food) and specifies measures for their control. The system consists of the following seven principles (cf. Codex Alimentarius Commission, 2001):

PRINCIPLE 1   Conduct a hazard analysis. *Prepare a flow diagram of the steps in the process. Identify and list the hazards with their causes and specify the control measures.*

PRINCIPLE 2   Determine the critical control points (CCPs). *A decision tree can be used.*

PRINCIPLE 3   Establish critical limit(s) *which must be met to ensure that each CCP is under control.*

PRINCIPLE 4   Establish a system to monitor control of the CCP *by scheduled testing or observations.*

PRINCIPLE 5   Establish the corrective action to be taken when monitoring indicates that a particular CCP is not under control *or is moving out of control.*

PRINCIPLE 6   Establish procedures for verification to confirm that the HACCP is working effectively, *which may include appropriate supplementary tests, together with a review.*

PRINCIPLE 7   Establish documentation concerning all procedures and records appropriate to these principles and their application.

N.B. The wording given in italics is not included in the principles of HACCP as documented by the Codex Alimentarius Commission but is included here as additional explanatory notes.

SECTION 3: HOW TO SET UP AND CONDUCT A HACCP STUDY

3.1 How to conduct a HACCP study

The material in this section is based on procedures published by Codex Alimentarius Commission, 2001 and outlined by workers in this field including ILSI, 1997 and 1999; Mortimore and Wallace, 1998; Mayes and Mortimore, 2001 and National Advisory Committee on Microbiological Criteria for Foods, 1992 and 1997.

HACCP systems should be underpinned by adherence to general principles of food hygiene, appropriate industry codes of practice and appropriate food safety legislation. These prerequisite programmes are required to be in place prior to the application of the principles of HACCP.

It is recommended that companies introducing HACCP for the first time should keep the terms of reference simple, i.e. restricted to product safety issues only. The company must select the HACCP approach most applicable to their operation; they may decide to look at all products or process lines on an individual basis or they may combine similar products or processes into modules. Sector specific model systems may also be available to guide companies through the HACCP process.

In order to carry out a HACCP study, management will have to provide the necessary team members (see below) for a number of study periods. The study team is likely to meet several times depending on the complexity of the process under study and the number and types of hazards to be identified. Before any HACCP study begins, the team leader/chairperson must ensure that senior management of the company are committed to providing the necessary resource for the study to be completed and to implementing the findings of the study, including reviews and updates. Without such commitment there is no point in beginning a study.

When conducting a HACCP study the seven principles may be applied as fourteen stages as shown in Figure 1.

Figure 1

Stages in a HACCP Study

Stage 1   Define terms of reference/scope of the study

Stage 2   Select the HACCP team

Stage 3   Describe the product

Stage 4   Identify intended use

Stage 5   Construct a flow diagram

Stage 6   On-site confirmation of flow diagram

Stage 7   List all potential hazards associated with each process step, conduct a hazard analysis and consider any measures to control identified hazards

Stage 8   Determine CCPs

Stage 9   Establish critical limits for each CCP

Stage 10   Establish a monitoring system for each CCP

Stage 11   Establish a corrective action plan

Stage 12   Verification including validation

Stage 13   Review the HACCP system

Stage 14   Establish documentation and record keeping

Prerequisite Programmes

Within a food operation there will be many hazards or sources of contamination that are of a "generic" or site-wide nature, i.e. they may occur at many steps of the process and are not specific to a particular process step, e.g. environmental conditions.

The control of these "day-to-day" potential hazards is normally part of good manufacturing practice or good hygiene practice, i.e. they are a pre-requirement to HACCP, and they should be in place to underpin the HACCP system. The term "prerequisite programmes" is finding widespread use to describe these measures that provide the basic environmental and operating conditions that are necessary for the production of safe and wholesome foods. Loss of control could result in a low risk safety issue, an economic issue or a quality defect. The prerequisite programmes cover three key areas, namely the premises, personnel and product. Typical examples include:

- Premises - buildings should be located, constructed and maintained following the principles of good hygienic design; equipment should be constructed and installed following the principles of good hygienic design; preventative maintenance and calibration schedules should be in place; there should be established written procedures and schedules for cleaning equipment and the premises; an effective pest control programme should be in place; there should be effective control for chemicals; appropriate services (e.g. water, steam, ice) should be provided and maintained at an adequate quality.

- Personnel - there should be documented procedures for personal hygiene, including rules for protective clothing, a jewellery policy and handwashing rules; these should be followed by staff and visitors to the premises; there should be appropriate medical screening of food handlers and appropriate training of personnel.

- Product - there should be effective supplier approval with specifications for raw materials, including packaging; raw materials and finished products should be stored and delivered under clean conditions; materials and products should be recorded in a system that provides traceability and allows rapid and accurate recall; there should be specifications for finished products.

Further useful guidance may be found in relevant Codex documents, sector specific industry guides and codes of practice and legislation.

The prerequisite programmes provide a solid foundation on which the HACCP system can be based and thus are normally expected to be in place before the HACCP plan is developed. It is vital that the prerequisite programmes are confirmed as working effectively by the HACCP team, and routinely as part of the scheduled verification activities - the HACCP will fail if they are not maintained. The need for additional or improved prerequisite programmes may become apparent to the HACCP team during the hazard analysis (Stage 7); it is important for this reason that the HACCP team consider all hazards during this stage independent of the prerequisite programmes thought to be in place. There may be instances where hazards that are normally considered to be "site-wide", and thus managed by the prerequisite programmes, will need to be included in the HACCP plan at specific process steps, e.g. ensuring personal hygiene in a manual handling operation in a high care environment.

Effective prerequisite programmes enable the HACCP system to be focused on the significant product and process food safety hazards that require specific control to assure consumer safety. By "screening" out the general hazards, the identification of the true critical control points is made easier and may result in the identification of a relatively small number of CCPs that can be effectively managed.

Prerequisite programmes will need to be documented and records maintained.

Stage 1: Define terms of reference/Scope of the study

A HACCP study should be carried out on a specific product/process line or a specific range of activities. Products or processes may be grouped together using a modular approach. In order for the study to proceed quickly it is essential that the terms of reference are agreed and stated clearly at the outset. It is therefore necessary to define whether the HACCP study should consider biological, chemical or physical hazards (or any combination of these) in the food and whether product safety and/or microbiological quality aspects (i.e. spoilage) are to be considered. It is recommended that the hazards to be considered in the study are clearly defined, e.g. specific pathogenic organisms or specific physical hazards such as metal, glass and hard plastic.

The terms of reference must also clearly state whether product is to be judged safe at the point of despatch, or at the point of consumption by following clear storage and use instructions. The start point of the study should be clearly defined to include all raw materials and ingredients.

If the completed HACCP study is supported by, and interrelates with, other documents, e.g. prerequisite programmes or those that form part of a quality management system, relevant legislation, codes of practice, good manufacturing practice and HACCP reference documents, they should be stated in the terms of reference to help to clarify the relationship.

Stage 2: Select the HACCP team

A HACCP study will require the collection, collation and evaluation of technical data, examples of which are given in Stage 5, and it is best carried out by a multi-disciplinary team. The use of such teams is known to improve greatly the quality of data considered and therefore the quality of decisions reached. Where, in a small business, these skills have to be represented by one person it is recommended that they seek specialist external support or information, to ensure that the HACCP study is effective.

The team should be able to draw on the following skills:

- **A production specialist**: An individual who has responsibility for, or is closely involved with, the process under study. It is essential that this individual is able to contribute details of what actually happens on the production line throughout all shift patterns

- **A quality assurance/quality control specialist**: An individual who understands the microbiological and/or chemical hazards and associated risks for a particular product group. This can be a QA/QC manager, microbiologist or food scientist as appropriate

- **An engineer**: An individual who has a working knowledge of the hygienic design and engineering operation/performance of the process equipment under study

- **Others**: Other relevant specialists may be co-opted onto the team as necessary, e.g. buyers, operators, packaging and distribution experts, a hygiene specialist

A person knowledgeable in the HACCP technique should be nominated as chairperson/team leader of the team and be responsible for managing the study. Ideally the individual(s) responsible for producing the flow diagram (see Stage 5) should be chosen from the above specialists.

A technical secretary/facilitator will be needed who will take notes at HACCP team meetings. This can be one of the specialists.

Selection of the people with the correct skills is essential if the study is to succeed. Team members must have sufficient working knowledge of the process to be able to contribute to the discussion of what **actually happens** on the production line, particularly if this is not revealed by the flow diagram. It is preferable that no member of the team should have any line management responsibility for any other team member. The team should be small, 4-6 persons; however, further personnel may attend specific meetings.

The membership of the team should be documented.

Team members selected for their relevant skills and expertise will need to work together easily and closely to achieve the defined objective of the HACCP study.

In particular, before commencing a study, members may need training in:

- The principles of HACCP

- How to approach the analysis logically, systematically and in sufficient detail

- The benefits of the HACCP system

- The role it plays in product safety

The chairperson of the team should have experience of HACCP team work. When HACCP is first introduced into a company this experience may have to be gained externally, but as the HACCP system is applied within a company, team members can be trained by the original chairperson and themselves become chairpersons. In this way, training in both chairing HACCP teams and applying HACCP principles can 'cascade' throughout a business.

In the UK the HACCP Training Standards Steering Group has produced national standards for HACCP training at the Intermediate and Advanced levels. The Qualification and Curriculum Authority (QCA) has approved HACCP qualifications at both levels.

It is vital that the team is maintained, especially once the HACCP study has been developed. New members should be brought in to replace those who leave; they should also be trained.

If there is more than one team operating, the business could appoint a HACCP co-ordinator or a HACCP steering group to co-ordinate the working of the individual teams. This approach is commonly used where modular HACCP plan structures have been selected.

Stage 3: Describe the product

A full description of the finished product under study, or intermediate product if only part of the process is being looked at, should be prepared. The product should be defined in terms of the key parameters which influence the safety of the product, to be used at Stage 7:

- Composition (e.g. recipe, raw materials)
- Chemical and physical structure (e.g. A_w, pH, emulsion)
- Processing (e.g. has product been heated and to what extent) and/or other preservation method (e.g. brining)
- Packaging system (e.g. aseptic packaging)
- Storage and distribution conditions (e.g. is the product to be kept frozen or chilled)

- Required shelf life (e.g. stated "use by" date or "best-before" date) under prescribed conditions.
- Instructions for product use (e.g. storage, handling and cooking instructions)

Stage 4: Identify intended use

The intended use of the product by the customer or consumer and the consumer target groups should be defined to encompass any special considerations; for example, is the product designed for babies, young children or the elderly, and is the product ready-to-eat?

Stage 5: Construct a flow diagram

Prior to the Hazard Analysis beginning it is necessary to carefully examine the product/process under study and produce a flow diagram around which the study can be based. The format of the flow diagram is a matter of choice; there are no rules for presentation. However, each step in the process (including process delays, recycle/rework loops, from the selection of raw materials through to the processing, distribution, retail and customer handling) should be clearly outlined in the correct sequence, with sufficient technical data available for the study to proceed.

Examples of the supporting data may include, but are not necessarily limited to:

- Specifications for raw materials/ingredients and packaging (to include microbiological, chemical and physical data)

- Floor plans, equipment and services layout

- Time/temperature history of all raw materials, and intermediate and finished products, including potential for delay

- Flow conditions for liquids and solids

- Equipment design features (including the presence of void spaces)

- Efficacy of cleaning and disinfection procedures

- Environmental hygiene

- Personnel routes

- Routes of potential cross-contamination

- Routes of waste material removal

- High/low risk area segregation

- Personal hygiene practices

- Storage and distribution conditions

- Consumer use instructions

- Organisation chart identifying key food safety responsibilities

Stage 6: On-site confirmation of flow diagram

It is important that, for existing production lines, those personnel involved in the HACCP study confirm that each step in the flow diagram is an accurate representation of the operation. This should additionally include confirmation of activities during any night shift or weekend running of the operation. The flow diagram should be amended to take account of any deviations found from the original diagram. If the analysis is being applied to a proposed line, there will be no opportunity for confirmation. In such a case the team must ensure that the flow diagram represents the most likely processing options and check the actual line during pre-production runs.

Stage 7: List all potential hazards associated with each process step, conduct a hazard analysis and consider any measures to control the identified hazards (Principle 1)

Using the flow diagram as a guide, the HACCP team should list all the potential hazards as defined in the terms of reference that may be reasonably expected to occur at each step, from primary production, processing, manufacture and distribution until the point of consumption. The consideration should include all the hazards which may be present in the raw materials, hazards that may be introduced during the process (e.g. contamination from the equipment, environment or personnel) and hazards that survive the process step. The team should also consider the way in which the process is managed and what could realistically occur that may not be covered by the flow diagram (e.g. process delays, temporary storage). The condition of the food (i.e. intrinsic factors including pH, A_w, temperature) must also be considered because it might have an effect on the ability of biological, chemical and or physical agents to cause an adverse effect on health. This is a deliberate policy to ensure that all conceivable hazards are identified in a "brainstorming" session.

The HACCP team should next conduct a Hazard Analysis to determine which hazards are of such a nature that their elimination or reduction to acceptable levels is essential to the production of safe food. The significance of any hazard to the final food safety of the finished product will need to be assessed, particularly when deciding on the control measures to be implemented. The source or cause of the hazard will need to be clearly defined.

This approach will ensure that the controls which represent reasonable precautions are put in place. In practice, the decision process will need to take into account the risk associated with any hazard identified. Considerations will always include a combination of the following:

- The likelihood of the hazard occurring and its consequent effects - e.g. previous company/industry experience or complaints, epidemiological data

- The severity of the hazard - e.g. life-threatening/mild; chronic/acute

- Numbers potentially exposed to the hazard - e.g. lot size; distribution

- Age/vulnerability of those exposed - e.g. young/elderly; allergies

- Survival or multiplication of microorganisms of concern

- Production or persistence in foods of toxins, chemicals or physical agents

- Source or cause of the hazard or conditions leading to the above

As a result of the increased emphasis given in the World Trade Organisation's Sanitary and Phytosanitary (SPS) agreement (1994) to the use of risk assessment, data will become increasingly available from Microbiological Risk Assessment which can be useful in Hazard Analysis and determining the stringency of HACCP plans. Currently, judgements are likely to be made based on qualitative data as listed above.

No attempt is made at this stage to identify Critical Control Points. Records of the hazard analysis should be maintained, including those hazards that were discounted.

The HACCP team must then consider what control measures, if any, exist which can be applied for each hazard. Control measures are those actions and/or activities that are required to prevent hazards, eliminate hazards or reduce their occurrence to an acceptable level.

More than one control may be required to control a specific hazard that occurs at different parts of the production/process. For example, if the hazard is the presence of *Listeria monocytogenes* in an ingredient/raw material which can be heat treated, pasteurization could be an appropriate control measure. The same hazard, *L.monocytogenes*, but arising from environmental contamination during ingredient assembly of a chilled product given no further heat treatment, requires other control measures, e.g. the prerequisite of barrier hygiene and holding the packaged product at an appropriate chilled temperature.

In some processes, however, one control measure at a single CCP will control more than one hazard (e.g. pasteurization or cooking may reduce both *Salmonella* and *Listeria* numbers to an acceptable level).

Control measures need to be underpinned by the prerequisite programmes.

Redesign or modification of the process may need to be considered.

Stage 8: Determine Critical Control Points (CCPs) (Principle 2)

CCPs are those steps of the process that are essential to prevent or eliminate food safety hazards or reduce them to acceptable levels. The identification of CCPs requires professional judgement and **may** be aided by the application of a decision tree. A number of decision trees have been developed, primarily with the aim of making the sequence of questions more user friendly (an example of a decision tree is given in Figure 2).

When using a decision tree, each process step identified in the flow diagram must be considered in sequence. At each process step, the decision tree must be applied to each of the identified hazards in turn.

The decision tree should not be used for those hazards that are managed by the prerequisite programmes, as the prerequisite programmes are vital and MUST be kept in place and operational as specified. The team must record that a particular hazard is managed by the prerequisite programmes.

Application of a decision tree will determine whether or not the process step is a CCP for each specific identified hazard. Although there is no limit on the number of CCPs that may be identified in a study, in practice there may only be a few.

Application of a decision tree should be flexible and requires common sense. This is particularly important when considering the impact of practices/procedures that could realistically occur but which may not be detailed in the flow diagram. As it is evident from the "comments on questions 1-4" (pages 19-21), access to technical data will be necessary to answer the questions in the decision tree.

It should be noted that a decision tree is equally applicable to the identification of CCPs for chemical and physical (i.e. foreign body) hazards.

Records of the use of the decision tree should be maintained.

Training in the application of a decision tree is recommended.

Figure 2

A CCP Decision Tree

The decision tree should not be used if the hazard is managed by the prerequisite programmes. Answer each question in sequence at each process step for each identified hazard.

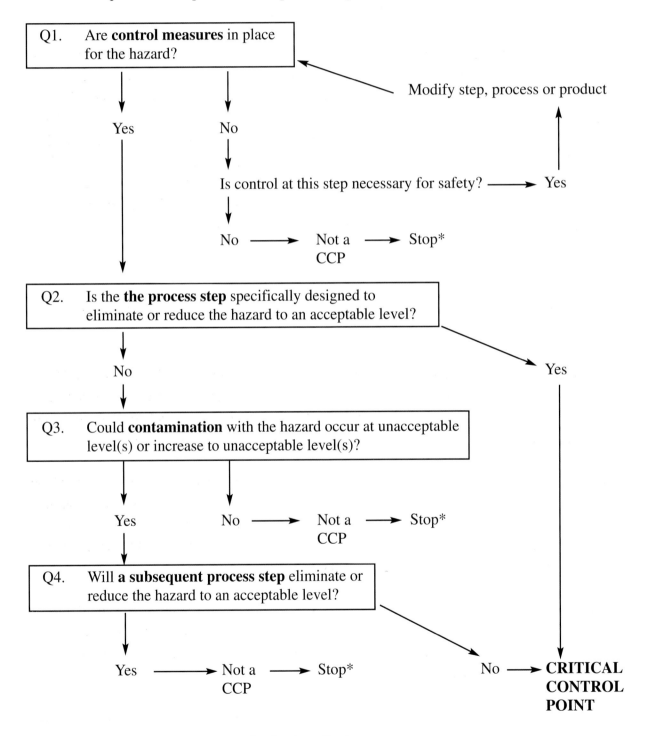

* Proceed to next hazard or step in the described process

Comments on questions 1-4 of the CCP Decision Tree shown in Figure 2

Q1: Are control measures in place for the hazard?

If the answer is *YES* the team should then consider Q2.

If the answer is *NO* (i.e. control measures are not in place for the hazard) the team must ask a supplementary question to determine if control is necessary at this step for product safety. If control is not necessary then the step is not a CCP and the team should apply the decision tree to the next identified hazard. If, however, the answer to this supplementary question is *YES*, then it is necessary to modify the step, process or product so that control is obtained over the specified hazard. During the analysis, the team may recommend a number of changes to the step, process or product that would allow control to be achieved and the analysis to proceed. Prior to the next formal meeting of the team, agreement must be reached with senior management that an appropriate change is acceptable and will be implemented.

Q2: Is the process step specifically designed to eliminate or reduce the hazard to an acceptable level?

The team should use the flow diagram data to answer this question for each process step. The question will identify those process steps that are specifically designed to eliminate or reduce the hazard to an acceptable level. Acceptable and unacceptable levels should be defined within the overall objectives in identifying the critical control points of the HACCP plan.

When considering this question for microbiological hazards the team should take account of the appropriate product technical data (e.g. pH, A_w, level and type of preservatives, dimensions of particulates, water droplet size) as well as the physical process being applied. Pasteurisation, cooking, aseptic packing, evisceration, preservative content and product structure are examples of process steps that could be microbiological CCPs in the right context.

If the team consider the answer to Q2 to be *YES* then the process step under consideration is a CCP. The team must identify precisely **what is critical** [i.e. is it an ingredient, a process step(s), the location or a practice/ procedure associated with the process step(s)] before applying the decision tree to the next process step.

If the answer to Q2 is *NO* then Q3 must be considered for the same process step and hazard.

Q3: Could contamination with the hazard occur at unacceptable level(s) or increase to unacceptable level(s)?

The team should consider the flow diagram data and their own working knowledge of the process, to answer this question. The team should first consider whether any of the ingredients used could conceivably contain any of the hazards under discussion in excess of acceptable levels. In doing so the team should take account of epidemiological data, previous supplier performance etc. If the team are unsure of the answer to this part of the question they should assume the *YES* response.

The team should also consider whether the immediate processing environment (e.g. people, equipment, air, walls, floors, drains) may be a source of the hazard under study and thereby contaminate the product. Once again the team should assume the *YES* response unless they are confident that the answer is *NO*.

When considering a possible increase in levels of the hazard, the team should be aware that it is possible that a single process step will not allow development of the hazard to unacceptable levels, but over a number of process steps the amount of increase may reach unacceptable levels due to the cumulative time and temperature of holding the product during processing. The team must therefore take account of not only the specific process step under discussion, but also the accumulated effect of subsequent process steps when answering the question. The team should include consideration of the following:

- Are the ingredients used likely to be a source of the hazard under study?

- Is the process step carried out in an environment likely to be a source of the hazard?

- Is cross-contamination from another product/ingredient possible?

- Is cross-contamination from personnel possible?

- Are there any void spaces in equipment that will enable product to stagnate and allow increase of the hazard to unacceptable levels?

- Are the cumulative time/temperature conditions such that the hazard will increase in the product to unacceptable levels?

N.B. This list is not exhaustive and the team should consider any factor or combination of factors associated with the process/product which could increase the hazards to an unacceptable level.

If after taking account of all the factors the team are confident that the answer to Q3 is *NO*, then this step is not a CCP and the team should apply the decision tree to the next process step or hazard. If the answer to Q3 is *YES*, then the team should consider Q4 for the same process step.

Q4: Will a subsequent process step eliminate or reduce the hazard to an acceptable level?

Question 4 will only be considered if the team believe the answer to Q3 to be *YES*. The team must then proceed sequentially through the remaining process steps of the flow diagram and determine if any subsequent processing step(s) will eliminate the hazard or reduce it to an acceptable level. Correct consumer use must be included here if the product is being judged "safe at the point of consumption".

Question 4 has a very important function when identifying CCPs, which is to allow the presence of a hazard at a process step if that hazard will subsequently be eliminated or reduced to an acceptable level, either as part of the process, or by the consumer's actions (e.g. by cooking). If this is not done, every process step in an operation might be regarded as critical leading to too many CCPs for an effective, practical control system.

Questions 3 & 4 are designed to work in tandem. For example, the presence of *Salmonella* in a raw meat ingredient for a ready-to-eat product prior to the cooking stage may be of concern but is not likely to be a CCP because the product will be cooked during processing. However, the control of *Salmonella* in garnishes added to that same product after cooking would be regarded as a CCP because no subsequent process steps would eliminate the *Salmonella* or reduce the likely occurrence to an acceptable level.

If the team judge that the answer to Q4 is *YES* they should then apply the decision tree to the next hazard, or to the next process step.

If the answer to Q4 is *NO* then a CCP has been identified. In this case, the team must identify precisely what is critical, i.e. is it a raw material, a process step(s), the location or a practice/procedure associated with the process step(s). When identified, the decision is made as to whether the existing control measure is sufficient.

N.B. The above questions assume application of the decision tree to an existing process. The decision tree can equally well be applied to new process/product development. In this case control measures would not be in place and the HACCP team would have to ask if such controls were available or use the analysis to specify controls that would be required for the new process/product.

Stage 9: Establish critical limits for each CCP (Principle 3)

Having identified all CCPs in the product/process under study, the team should then proceed to identify critical limits for the control measure(s) at each CCP. The critical limit is the criterion which separates acceptability from unacceptability or safe product from unsafe product. Some are defined in legislation, e.g. temperature and time to be used for pasteurisation, whilst some may need experimental data to be collected to determine the critical limit or advice from specialists with expert knowledge. For many practical purposes, a target level may be specified which is the pre-determined value for the control measure applied at each CCP with the tolerance indicating the degree of latitude allowable.

The specific critical limit, target level and tolerance set for each CCP/control measure must represent some measurable parameter related to the CCP. Those that can be measured or observed relatively quickly and easily are preferred. Examples of these include measurement of temperature, time, moisture level, pH, A_w; chemical analyses; visual assessments of product and management/operational practices.

Details of the establishment of the critical limits should be recorded.

Stage 10: Establish a monitoring system for each CCP (Principle 4)

Selection of the correct monitoring system is an essential part of any HACCP study. Monitoring is a planned sequence of observations or measurements of CCP control measures. The monitoring system describes the methods by which the business is able to confirm that all CCPs are operating within the defined critical limit (i.e. are 'in control') and it also produces an accurate record of performance for future use in verification (see Stage 12).

Monitoring procedures must be able to detect loss of control at the CCP. Ideally monitoring should provide this information in time for corrective action to be taken to regain control of the process before there is a need to segregate or reject product, but unfortunately this is not always possible. Monitoring systems may be either on-line, e.g. time/temperature measurements, or off-line, e.g. measurement of salt, pH, A_w, total solids. On-line systems give an immediate indication of performance. Off-line systems require monitoring to be carried out away from the production line and occasionally may result in a very long time period elapsing before results are available and action can be taken. This may not be appropriate for all food products, e.g. chilled foods.

Microbiological monitoring systems have the extra disadvantage of having to interpret the results in the light of the known (or unknown) distribution of organisms in the product and are therefore seldom suitable as monitoring systems for CCPs.

Monitoring systems may also be continuous (e.g. recording continuous process temperatures on a thermograph) or discontinuous (e.g. sample collection and analysis). Continuous systems provide a dynamic picture of performance whilst discontinuous systems must ensure that the discrete sample monitored is representative of the bulk product.

In an ideal situation, a monitoring system should be chosen that gives an on-line continuous monitor of performance and responds dynamically to correct changes exceeding the specified tolerance, but in the practical situation the choice of monitoring systems available for a particular CCP may often be quite limited. Whichever monitoring system is chosen, the team must ensure that the results obtained are directly relevant to the CCP and that any limitations are fully understood. Physical, chemical and sensory monitoring methods are preferred because of their speed of response.

In addition to identifying the most appropriate monitoring system, the team should address the following issues:

WHO is to act?

The HACCP team should specify the job title of the individual(s) responsible for performing the monitoring. This person must have the knowledge and authority to take corrective action if the critical limit is not achieved (see Stage 11). All records and documents associated with monitoring CCPs should be signed by the person doing the monitoring and by a responsible designated person who reviews the stated results.

WHEN are they to act?

If monitoring is not continuous then the frequency of monitoring must be specified and must be sufficient to ensure that control is being exercised at the CCP.

HOW are they to act?

Monitoring procedures need to be underpinned by detailed specifications and procedures to ensure their effective implementation. Included will be a detailed description of precisely how the monitoring is to be carried out. The details should be relevant to the type of monitoring being carried out, e.g. temperature measurements for a heating process should be made at the coldest (i.e. slowest heating) point of the product, whilst temperature measurements for a cooling process should be made at the warmest (i.e. slowest cooling) part. This requirement means that the designated operators must be trained to understand their monitoring functions and how to carry them out correctly.

Failure to achieve a critical limit is termed a deviation and the appropriate corrective action must be initiated, see Stage 11.

See also Implementation, section 3.2.7 (page 32-38).

Stage 11: Establish a corrective action plan (Principle 5)

The team should specify the actions to be taken either when monitoring results show that, at a CCP, there has been a failure to meet the critical limit or, preferably, what action should be taken when monitoring results indicate a trend towards loss of control. In the latter case, action may be taken to bring the process back into control before it leads to a deviation.

Disposition or, if appropriate, rework actions need to be taken with food that has been produced during the time period that the CCP was 'out of control'.

The cause of the deviation should be investigated; appropriate and timely remedial action should be performed.

Both corrective action and disposition/rework actions should be documented in the HACCP record keeping and the responsibility clearly assigned.

Stage 12: Verification including validation (Principle 6)

This stage comprises two distinct activities:
• Validation
• Verification

Validation

The contents of the HACCP plan must be validated prior to implementation. The main objectives of validation are to ensure that the hazards identified in the study are complete and correct, and that the selected controls are suitable, i.e. hazards can be effectively managed if the stated requirements are followed.

A team may be required to perform the validation; this may consist of the HACCP study team plus additional internal or external specialists. The team should evaluate evidence supporting the selection, or exclusion, of significant hazards, the determination of the CCPs, the setting of the critical limits and that the monitoring and corrective action activities will be adequate to assure food safety.

Testing may be performed at the controls to check their effectiveness, both prior to implementation and periodically thereafter. Examples of validation testing would include thermal evaluation, temperature distribution, challenge testing and mathematical modelling.

Validation should include the formal sign-off of the HACCP plan by the person ultimately responsible for product safety management at the business.

Verification

The HACCP study team should put into place procedures that can be used to demonstrate compliance with the validated HACCP plan and to determine its effectiveness once in use.

There are two main aspects of verification, firstly demonstrating conformance (i.e. personnel are following the stated procedures/work instructions) and secondly gathering information that the HACCP system and prerequisites are effective (i.e. safety requirements are being met).

Verification should examine the entire HACCP system including all CCPs and its records. The HACCP study team should specify the methods and frequency of verification procedures. Verification activities may include internal/external auditing systems, microbiological and chemical examinations of intermediate and finished product samples, more searching/vigorous tests at selected CCPs, surveys of the market place for unexpected health/spoilage problems associated with the product and updated data on consumer use of the product. The findings of customer visits and analysis of customer complaints can also form part of the verification procedures.

Examples of key verification procedures include:

- Internal/external review of the HACCP study and its records

- A review of deviations, product dispositions and corrective actions

- Audits of records and associated procedures at CCPs to observe if CCPs are under control

Figure 3

Sequence for Validation and Verification Activities

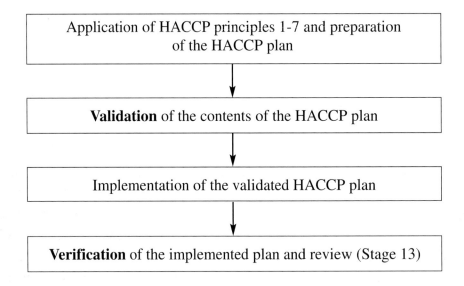

Stage 13: Review the HACCP system

The HACCP study team should perform a periodic review, the freqency of which should be established based on the 'risk' of the product and its intended use; typically this should be at least annually. In addition, it is necessary to have a mechanism in place that will automatically trigger a review of the HACCP system by the HACCP team prior to any changes which may affect overall product safety.

It is essential that any of the following should automatically be assessed to determine if a review is required:

- Change in raw material/product formulation

- Change in raw material supplier

- Change in processing system

- Change in factory layout and environment

- Modification to process equipment

- Change in cleaning and disinfection programme

- Failures in the system, e.g. corrective actions and the need for product recall

- Change in packaging, storage and distribution system

- Change in staff levels and/or responsibilities

- Anticipated change in customer/consumer use

- Receipt of information from the market place indicating a health risk associated with the product

- Emergence of foodborne pathogens with public health significance

N.B. This list is not exhaustive.

Data arising from HACCP reviews must be documented and form part of the HACCP record keeping system. Any changes arising from a HACCP review must be fully incorporated into the HACCP plan and may need to be validated. This is because these changes may mean that certain CCP control measures or specified tolerances have been changed and/or additional CCPs or control measures have been put in place. It is essential for a user to be sure that accurate up-to-date information is available from the records. Additionally, valuable resources used to establish HACCP will not be wasted because the current documentation is out-of-date and therefore of doubtful value. A system of management for the maintenance of the HACCP system is therefore required and its proper operation is essential.

The results of HACCP reviews should be brought to the attention of senior management.

Stage 14: Establish documentation and record keeping (Principle 7)

Efficient and accurate record keeping is essential to the successful application of HACCP to a food operation. It is important for a food operation to be able to demonstrate that the principles of HACCP have been correctly applied, and that documentation and records have been kept in a way appropriate to the nature and size of the operation. Documentation of HACCP procedures at all process steps should be assembled and included in a manual and/or integrated into a controlled Quality Management System. Software systems are available to assist in the documentation of HACCP plans.

Examples of documentation include:

- Documentation of the system (e.g. the HACCP plan, details of the hazard analysis, CCP determination, critical limit determination)

- Procedures and work instructions

and should be supported by records.

The HACCP plan must contain:

- The terms of reference/scope of the study
- The team members
- Product description
- Intended use of the product
- Flow diagram
- Relevant hazards and controls
- The CCPs that have been determined
- The critical limits at the CCPs, with targets and tolerances where relevant
- The monitoring plan for each CCP
- The corrective action plan
- Details of verification activities, including details of scheduled review
- Date of validation
- Reference to relevant procedures, records, forms.

Some operations have found it useful to additionally develop a CCP summary chart that just details the hazards, controls, critical limits, monitoring and corrective action activities at the CCPs. However, this must not replace the full HACCP plan.

Examples of supporting records include:

- Details of the team members, their roles within the team and their relevant skills/experience
- Nature, source and quality of raw materials
- Complete processing records, including storage and distribution
- All decisions reached relating to product safety, e.g. the hazard analysis, CCP and critical limit determinations
- Monitoring records
- Deviations file
- Corrective actions and product disposition records
- Prerequisite programmes including cleaning and disinfection records
- Food safety policy
- Modification file
- Verification and validation data (see Stage 12)
- Review data (see Stage 13)

The length of time records should be retained may vary. In the European Union, a number of product specific hygiene directives contain requirements relating to record keeping in connection with food safety management systems. Generally, they require a minimum 2 year retention period for records of controls, monitoring and any sampling carried out. For products that cannot be stored at ambient temperatures, the retention period is reduced to 2-6 months after the expiry of shelf life, the time period varying depending on the applicable directive (or national implementing regulations). The retention period for records should be considered in light of the above and in the context of supporting a defence of due diligence.

All records must be accurate, genuine and legible.

The food operation should have in place a document control procedure to ensure effective control of all relevant documentation.

3.2   Hints and warnings

The following notes set out some of the points of management and discipline that need to be addressed in setting up and conducting a HACCP programme.

3.2.1 Commitment

It is essential that the full commitment of all levels of management is obtained in order that relevant personnel are freed from other duties for the necessary time and that the output of the HACCP study will be implemented.

3.2.2 Preparation

Preparation must be thorough and well in advance of the formal meetings of the HACCP team. Such preparation should include:

- Circulation of an outline of what is to be achieved, the process and product to be considered and a proposed method of working

- Confirmation of the constitution of the HACCP team. It is important that the team contains all of the necessary disciplines and experience, and it is not acceptable that one nominee will cover a colleague's areas to save management time

- Provision of a suitable meeting room and facilities

- Assurance that, with the exception of real emergencies, there will be no interruptions, including telephone calls

- Early consideration of available software packages to assist in the study and its implementation

3.2.3 Documentation

Documentation should be prepared in advance of the first formal meeting to cover the following areas:

- Intended product use; product description and specifications; product formulations including permitted tolerances (e.g. pH, A_w, preservative addition); packaging type (e.g. modified/controlled atmosphere, vacuum) and intended distribution conditions (cold chain or ambient)

- Process details including relevant engineering data (e.g. heat treatment given, cooling rates, times held at specific temperatures)

- Sanitation/housekeeping procedures

- Outline flow diagrams for the process that include relevant services interactions, such as water, steam, vacuum and gas supplies

- Intended process equipment, production line layout, processing environment and building materials of construction

This and any other relevant technical information should be prepared by delegated members of the team in advance of the formal meetings to avoid unnecessary interruptions for the *ad hoc* collection of various facts and data.

3.2.4 HACCP team meetings

It is important that all team members get to the meetings at the prearranged time and have organised their other duties in such a way that full attention can be given to the job in hand. Before the HACCP study starts it is useful to confirm the following points:

- A timetable - it is beneficial to prearrange suitable breaks so that 'held' messages and telephone calls can, if essential, be dealt with

- A chairperson should be appointed. The chairperson need not be a specialist in any of the disciplines required but MUST have a thorough working knowledge of HACCP and be experienced in leading and recording HACCP studies. To help ensure ownership of the completed HACCP system it is recommended that the representative from production should be the chairperson.

- An outline of the intended programme of work should be given which includes confirmation of the product/process under review and the intended scope of the HACCP study

- If the HACCP team is relatively inexperienced it is advisable to limit the scope to simplify and make it more manageable - e.g. consider pathogens in a single product

- A review of available information to establish whether there is a need to call for further records or additional assistance

3.2.5 The HACCP study

It is essential that the meetings allow a disciplined and thorough consideration of all relevant information. It is often useful to decide at the outset to tackle the job in discrete process sections (based on outline flow diagrams) so that a step-by-step approach can be established.

Other points to remember are:

- Company, sector or national generic plans may be used for guidance; however, the information must be fully checked for applicability to the actual operation as it is very unlikely that two operations will be identical in all respects

- Do not make assumptions.
  Process and product formulation details must be confirmed before any meaningful hazard analysis can be started. Such confirmation may be by discussion or may involve an examination of the relevant part of the process 'in action' to verify facts

- Challenge 'beliefs'.
  Confirm that what is believed to be happening is in fact the case. This consideration must extend to process conditions (e.g. times, temperatures), as well as to production sequences (e.g. product lines, holding tanks). Confirm that beliefs are true over all production shifts, weekend breaks, etc.

- Avoid any tendency to make the analysis 'fit'.
  In considering what is currently being done in the area of control, avoid the trap 'we test for it so it must be a CCP', or even more serious, the reverse situation

- Avoid any tendency to distort the analysis in an attempt to make it compatible with other systems that might already be in place

- Avoid the situation where the chairperson dominates discussions and decisions and therefore stifles other inputs

- Consider all inputs properly. Position in the management hierarchy is not relevant. It is the quality of the information contributed by the team which is important.

- Do not be tempted to rush the job because the team is running out of time at a meeting. If necessary, agree to reconvene at a later date if the job cannot be properly completed in the allocated time

- Keep a record of all points discussed as well as notes of the agreed analysis

3.2.6 After the study

- Ensure that a full record of the agreed analysis is prepared and circulated to the HACCP team in draft form for comments and amendment. This stage should be completed as soon as possible after the formal meeting

- Set a deadline for comments on drafts

- Issue a 'final' copy immediately after the comments deadline date

  It is worth noting that the completed HACCP study may be issued as part of a total quality management scheme with controlled documentation and also forms the basis for site auditing purposes

- Set a timetable and procedures for review and update of the HACCP plan

3.2.7 Implementation

To be useful, it is clear that the HACCP plan developed by the HACCP team must be successfully incorporated into the manufacturing operations of the company. In order to achieve such implementation, a number of key practical steps are necessary.

- Validation

Prior to implementation it is necessary that the conclusions reached in the HACCP plan are validated. Are the control measures specified capable of eliminating or controlling the identified hazards to an acceptable level? The subject of validation is dealt with at Stage 12 (see pages 24-25).

- Documentation of HACCP information

For each control, monitoring and corrective action activity there should be a documented procedure that fully defines the actions to be taken and the records to be kept. These could vary in complexity from the detailed procedure for the operation of a continuous steriliser, to the more simple procedure required for the measurement of pH. Once there are documented procedures, then the operators responsible for carrying them out should be suitably trained against the requirements contained within the procedure.

Clearly different personnel may be involved in these various processes and so it is important that procedures also specify the company function responsible for each individual part of the process (for example, production, quality control, quality assurance).

It is assumed that a company will have some system for document identification. To reinforce the understanding of the importance of the HACCP plan, the plan itself should cross reference to the relevant procedures and record sheets.

The "conventional" tabular format for presentation of HACCP plans is very useful in providing an immediate overview of the entirety of the study and in particular of the CCPs and control measures employed. It may be limited in usefulness in terms of providing for the needs of manufacturing as there is limited space in the tabular forms for the inclusion of great detail. An alternative method is to present the HACCP plan with each process step on a sheet, allowing space for the inclusion of sufficient detail. Examples of both methods are provided in Figures 4 and 5.

Figure 4. Example extract from a tabular format HACCP plan

Process step	CCP No.	Hazards	Control measures	Critical limit	Monitoring procedures	Corrective action	Records
Double seaming of filled cans	CCP 5	Post process microbial contamination leading to growth	Defined maintenance of seaming machine *(Procedure cm/CCP5/01 Machine manual, edition 2)*	To maintenance schedule, daily, weekly, monthly	Daily inspection of maintenance records *(Procedure QA/MP/01v)*	Re-training of maintenance staff *(Procedure T/CCP5/01)*	Seamer maintenance record sheet *(R/CCP5/01)*
			Cans closed according to double seam specification *(Procedure cm/CCP5/02)*	Limits defined for actual overlap, tightness rating and % BHB *(Data sheet ds/CCP5/01)*	Seams measured before start up and every 4 hours *(Procedure QA/CCP5/01)*	Actions defined in procedure *(Procedure ca/CCP5/01)*	Seam measurement record sheet *(R/CCP5/02* and *Corrective action sheet R/CCP5/05)*
			Training of personnel involved in seaming machine operation and seam measurement *(T/CCP5/01)*	All personnel trained according to relevant procedures	Check signatures are of authorised personnel on seaming machine and and seam record sheets	Provide re-training and ensure only authorised personnel carry out seam related functions	Training record sheet *(TR/01)*

Figure 5. Extract from a non-tabular format HACCP plan

CCP No. 5

Process Step No. 10 Double seaming of filled cans

Hazard | Post process microbial contamination leading to growth as a result of poor quality double seams

Control measures | Double seaming machines are maintained according to defined service procedure, *Procedure cm/CCP5/01*
Seamer machine manual, edition 2.

Cans are closed according to can maker's specified tolerances for actual overlap, tightness rating and % body hook butting (BHB).
Procedure for seamer operation cm/CCP5/02
Seam specification data sheet ds/CCP5/01

Personnel involved in seaming machine operation and seam measurement are suitably trained.
Procedure for training of seamer personnel T/CCP5/01

Critical limits | Seams are closed to comply with critical limits included within data sheet ds/CCP5/01 for relevant size of can.
Critical values for seam acceptability include those for:
- % body hook butting
- Actual overlap
- % overlap
- Free space
- Seam tightness rating

Monitoring procedures | Monitoring procedures are designed to check compliance with specification and include:
- Continual visual and tactile checking of seams by crate filler operator
  Procedure QA/CCP5/02
- Recorded visual checking of 10 cans per seaming head at 1/2-hourly intervals by QA technician
  Procedure QA/CCP5/03
- Seam analysis by both projection and tear down, for each seaming head, at start up and at 4-hourly intervals
  Procedure QA/CCP5/01

Corrective action
In the event that critical seam measurements are observed to fall outside the specified values the sequence of events should follow the corrective action procedure. This requires

- The immediate rechecking of results obtained
- Notification of specified Production, Engineering and QA personnel
- Stopping of production
- Identification and isolation of affected material
- Resolution of the immediate situation and restart of manufacture
- Resolution of the safety of affected cans
- Corrective action procedure *ca/CCP5/01*

Record keeping
The following forms are required for completion

- Seamer machine maintenance sheet *R/CCP5/01*
- Double seam visual inspection report *R/CCP5/03*
- Double seam projection analysis and tear down report *R/CCP5/02*
- Double seam non-compliance report R/CCP5/04
- Double seam corrective action report *R/CCP5/05*
- Seamer personnel training record *TR/01*

Verification procedure
Procedure for the verification of the correct application of CCP No. 5 *vp/CCP5/01*

- Involvement of operational personnel

The responsibility for the everyday practical implementation of the HACCP plan rests with the line operators and supervisors together with the relevant production managers who have the final overall responsibility for ensuring that operations take place in the defined manner. It is important that all such personnel receive training both in relation to the importance of the HACCP system in general and also in relation to the specific control, monitoring and corrective action procedures for which they are directly responsible. Clearly if operations staff are involved or consulted in the development of the HACCP plans and the accompanying procedures it will help their understanding of the HACCP system and register the importance of the processes under their control in relation to product safety.

- Training

It is recommended that all personnel should be informed about:

- The reason why the HACCP plan was developed
- The role of those involved in the development of the plan
- The support given by management to maintain the system

Basic familiarisation on food safety management should be provided to all production based personnel during induction training and as refresher courses at relevant intervals in order to provide understanding on:

- sources of hazards and their effect on food safety
- critical control points and their role in the assurance of product safety
- control measures at critical control points for which they may be responsible
- critical limits for the controlled parameters
- monitoring procedures and the importance of accurate record keeping
- the corrective actions to be applied if monitoring indicates that critical limits are exceeded or there is a trend towards loss of control
- the objective of verification procedures.

Specific operational training should be made in relation to the procedures or work instructions to which each individual will be working.

Training should involve both formal discussion and practical demonstration as appropriate. It is important that all personnel understand their roles and responsibilities in relation to the HACCP plan. Training may be needed in the interpretation of data produced during monitoring operations, especially if a new procedure is introduced; skills training may be needed if a new method of measurement is introduced.

Full training records should be maintained, which indicate the procedures against which training has been provided, and should be signed off by both the trainer and the trainee.

- System visibility in practice

In application, the HACCP system should be visible within the manufacturing environment in order to continue to emphasise that HACCP provides the practical means for safe manufacture and is part of the daily business of the company. Measures taken to provide such visibility may include:

- indication on all relevant procedure documents of the CCP to which they apply
- colour coding of procedure documents describing operations associated with CCPs
- inclusion of CCP reference numbers on all associated record forms
- inclusion of target values and tolerances on all relevant record forms
- attachment of permanent tags or labels to items of equipment indicating the CCP number to which they correspond.

- Quality plans

The working document for quality measurement is the quality plan. This is the comprehensive schedule of measurements taken in order to provide assurance of product quality and safety. It will detail the sampling carried out, frequency of test, methods used and specifications for measured values. All items included in the HACCP plan and requiring measurement should be included in the quality plan. There will also be items that relate to quality attributes, rather than food safety.

- Maintenance of the HACCP plans

It should be recognised that companies are dynamic organisations and that processes, plants and products are likely to change with time. Hence if the HACCP plans are to continue to be effective they must be continually renewed and updated to reflect any changed situation, as described in Stage 13 (see pages 26-27).

In addition all levels of personnel should be encouraged to suggest modifications for consideration by the HACCP team as necessary.

3.3   HACCP and ISO 9001:2000

HACCP could be managed as part of a quality management system; this may be a formal system based on the International Standard.

The international series of standards for Quality Management Systems (ISO 9000 series) underwent a major revision in 2000. The ISO 9001:2000 standard now focuses closely on meeting the customers' needs and expectations, as well as the requirement for continual improvement of the implemented quality management system. The requirements of the Standard promote the adoption of a process approach to the development and implementation of a quality management system, i.e. the interaction of 'inputs' with 'outputs' and their effective management.

The Standard details a number of specific requirements in sections entitled documentation, management responsibility, resource management, product realisation, measurement, analysis and improvement.

Guidelines published on the application of the Standard for the food and drink industry (BS ISO 15161:2001) show the relationship between the seven principles of HACCP and the subclauses of ISO 9001:2000 which particularly support or align to the HACCP principles.

HACCP is not only complementary to a quality management system based on ISO 9001:2000, but a combination of the principles used by both is considered by many to strengthen the overall food safety assurance system that results.

SECTION 4: WORKED EXAMPLES

To demonstrate the application of the HACCP principles, examples based on actual studies are included in this section. It must be stressed that:

- The details given for each example are not exhaustive and verification activities are not included (see Stage 12, Section 3)

- The findings should not be taken as specific recommendations for similar processes

- The information is not intended for direct use in factory (processing) conditions, but only as a demonstration of how the HACCP principles can be applied

EXAMPLE 1: CHICKEN STUFFED WITH PRAWNS AND GARLIC
IN A WILD MUSHROOM AND WALNUT SAUCE

This example is used to illustrate the application of the principles to all steps in a food operation and to illustrate the use of a decision tree and the information shown in a HACCP plan. Cross references to the detailed control measures, monitoring procedures and corrective actions are not given. The responsibility for monitoring procedures is not shown. Verification procedures are not shown. Not all process steps have been included.

Terms of reference: The HACCP team decided to consider food safety hazards including pathogenic microorganisms, and specific chemicals, foreign bodies and allergens. Packaging material related aspects were included in a separate study. Ambient storage steps are addressed in a separate study.

Prerequisite programmes are in place and include supplier approval, pest control and planned maintenance.

Description of product: The product is a prepared meal containing chicken which is stuffed with a mixture of prawns and garlic puree prior to being cooked to achieve a minimum temperature of 80°C. The cooked, stuffed chicken is blast chilled on trays and manually placed in plastic product containers. A precooked (>95°C) sauce, of neutral pH, containing wild mushrooms and chopped walnuts is automatically hot deposited (>70°C) onto the stuffed, cooked chicken. The container is heat sealed with a plastic film top, inserted into final pre-printed packs and blast chilled. The product is stored and distributed at 2-5°C and is sold with a shelf life of 8 days from packing. The product is retailed at <8°C and is designed to be reheated prior to consumption.

Ingredients: Raw chicken, garlic puree, cooked peeled prawns, chopped walnuts, pasteurised milk, pasteurised cream, flour, salt, dried wild mushrooms and pepper.

Intended use: The product is a convenience meal which is suitable for consumption by all groups although it is likely to be consumed by adults.

HACCP team: The team included the production manager (team leader), hygiene supervisor, quality assurance manager (technical secretary), and "high risk area" shift manager, and co-opted the warehouse storeman during discussion of steps 11-20.

Figure 6: Example 1 Summary Process Flow Diagram: Chicken with Prawns and Garlic in a Wild Mushroom and Walnut Sauce

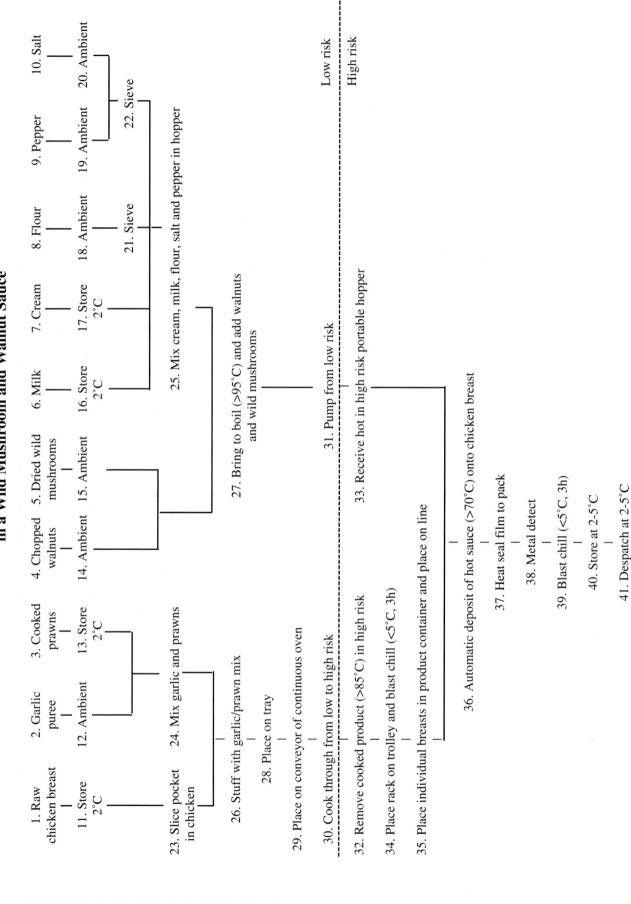

Table 1 Example 1: HACCP Chart for Chicken Stuffed with Prawns and Garlic in a Wild Mushroom and Walnut Sauce

Process step	Hazards	Control measures	CCP question 1	2	3	4	CCP	Critical limit	Monitoring procedures	Corrective action	Record
1 Intake of raw chicken breast (size controlled at supplier)	Presence of pathogens (e.g. *Salmonella, Campylobacter*)	Supplier Quality Assurance See Prerequisite Programme (cooking at Step 30)									
	Growth of toxigenic bacteria if temperature abused during delivery	Acceptance temperature	Y	N	Y	N	Yes	Limit:4°C on receipt Target:2°C on receipt	Temperature check of product before unloading	If >2°C but <4°C then check despatch temperature record of supplier. If loading temperature <4°C then accept. If >4°C then reject	Temperature checks
11 Chilled storage of raw chicken breast	Growth of toxigenic bacteria if temperature not controlled (*S. aureus, B. cereus, Cl. perfringens*)	Control of chiller temperature	Y	N	Y	N	Yes	Limit: 4°C Target: 2°C	Continuous monitoring of chiller temperature	If >4°C repair/adjust. If <4°C not achieved within 2 hours then move product to other chiller. If chiller >4°C then assess product temperature and reject products if >4°C	Temperature records Process deviations Corrective action and rechecks
	or growth of toxigenic psychrotrophic bacteria if shelf life exceeded (*Cl. botulinum*)	Limit of time from receipt of raw material to use	Y	N	Y	N	Yes	Limit: Use within 'use by' of raw material Target: Use within 2 days of receipt	Check date codes prior to use	If code missing or beyond 'use by' then dispose to waste	Raw material codes used
23 Slice pocket in chicken with knife	Breakage of metal blade	Visual inspection of knives before use (metal detection at Step 38)	Y	N	Y	Y	No				
2 Intake heat processed, ambient stable garlic puree	Presence of vegetative pathogens	Supplier Quality Assurance See Prerequisite Programme (cooking at Step 30)									
	or growth of spore forming toxigenic bacteria (e.g. *Cl. botulinum, B. cereus*)	Supplier Quality Assurance (specification for product formulation)	Y	N	Y	N	Yes	Limit: pH <4.5, a_w <0.93. Target: pH 4.2, a_w 0.91	Certificate of analysis Intake testing	If outside specification then reject batch and inform supplier	Certificates of analysis and in house analysis results

Table 1 Example 1: HACCP Chart for Chicken Stuffed with Prawns and Garlic in a Wild Mushroom and Walnut Sauce (Continued)

Process step	Hazards	Control measures	CCP question 1 2 3 4 CCP	Critical limit	Monitoring procedures	Corrective action	Record
3 Intake cooked prawns	Presence of pathogens	Supplier Quality Assurance See Prerequisite Programme (cooking at Step 30)					
	Growth of toxigenic bacteria if temperature abused	Acceptance temperature	Y N Y N Yes	Limit: 8°C on receipt Target: <5°C on receipt	Temperature check of product before unloading	If >5°C but <8°C then check despatch temperature record of supplier. If fill temperature <5°C then accept. If >8°C then reject	Temperature checks
13 Chilled storage of cooked prawns	Growth of toxigenic bacteria if temperature not controlled (e.g. S. aureus, Cl. perfringens)	Control of chiller temperature	Y N Y N Yes	Limit: 8°C Target: 2°C	Continuous monitoring of chiller temperature	If >8°C repair/adjust. If <8°C not achieved within 2 hours then move product to other chiller. If 8°C check temperature of product and if >8°C reject products	Temperature records Process deviations Corrective action and rechecks
	or growth of toxigenic, psychrotrophic bacteria if shelf life exceeded (Cl. botulinum)	Limit of time from receipt of raw material to use	Y N Y N Yes	Limit: use within 'use by' of raw material Target: use within 2 days of receipt	Check codes prior to use	If code missing or beyond 'use by' then dispose to waste	Raw material codes disposed of
24 Mix garlic and prawns	Growth of toxigenic bacteria due to temperature abuse and time delays due to production breakdowns	Control of room temperature	Y N Y N Yes	Room temperature: Limit: 15°C Target: 12°C	Continuous monitoring of room temperature	If >12°C repair/adjust. If <12°C not achieved within 2 hours then all product must be processed within 2 hours or remove product to chiller. If >15°C remove product to chill until temperature controlled	Temperature records Process deviations Corrective action and rechecks
		Control of time prior to cooking		Time during break-down: Limit 2 hours Target: 1 hour	During breakdown monitor time delay	If time during production breakdown >1 hour but <2 hour then remove product to chiller. If >2 hour then dispose product	Production break-down times and disposed product

Table 1 Example 1: HACCP Chart for Chicken Stuffed with Prawns and Garlic in a Wild Mushroom and Walnut Sauce (Continued)

Process step	Hazards	Control measures	CCP question 1 2 3 4	CCP	Critical limit	Monitoring procedures	Corrective action	Record
26 & 28 Stuff chicken with garlic and prawn mix and place chicken on tray	Growth of toxigenic bacteria due to temperature abuse and time delays due to product breakdowns	Control of room temperature	Y N Y N	Yes	Room temperature: Limit: 15°C Target: 12°C	Continuous monitoring of room temperature	If >12°C repair/adjust. If <12°C not achieved within 2 hours then all product must be processed within 2 hours or remove product to chiller. If >15°C remove product to chill until temperature controlled	Temperature records Process deviations Corrective action and rechecks
		Control of time prior to cooking			Time during breakdown: Limit: 2 hours Target: 1 hour	During breakdown monitor time delay	If time during production breakdown >1 hour but <2 hours then remove product to chiller. If >2 hours then dispose product	Production breakdown times and disposed product
29 & 30 Place tray on conveyor of continuous oven and cook	Survival of vegetative pathogens (e.g. *Campylobacter*, *Salmonella*) due to inadequate cooking	Cooking	Y Y	Yes	Oven temperature 200°C Belt speed to ensure residence of 15 minutes	Continuous monitoring of oven temperature and belt speed	If temperature low then stop belt and rectify. Once rectified re-cook and probe product (see below)	Temperature records Process deviations Corrective action and rechecks)
					Cold spot product temperature: Minimum: 80°C Target: 85°C	Temperature probing of cooked product (3 products per cook from different parts of the belt at 30 minute intervals)	If product <85°C but >80°C then review belt speed or oven temperature to achieve >85°C. If temperature <80°C then stop production, remove all product, correct oven temperature or belt speed and recook to achieve temperature	
32 Remove cooked in high risk area	Cross contamination with environmental contaminants (e.g. *Listeria*, *S. aureus*)	Scheduled cleaning	Y N Y N	Yes	Cleaning schedules adhered to	Visual inspection, ATP hygiene assessments	Reclean and retraining	Cleaning records and ATP results
		Barrier hygiene			Barrier hygiene rules must be followed	Visual inspection	Retraining, repeat entry following barrier rules	Training records

Table 1 Example 1: HACCP Chart for Chicken Stuffed with Prawns and Garlic in a Wild Mushroom and Walnut Sauce (Continued)

Process step	Hazards	Control measures	CCP question 1	2	3	4	CCP	Critical limit	Monitoring procedures	Corrective action	Record
34 Place rack on trolley and blast chill chicken	Growth of spore forming pathogens (*Cl. perfringens*) due to inadequate chilling	Blast chill	Y	Y	Y	N	Yes	Limit: <5°C, 4 hours Target: <5°C, 3 hours	Temperature probe of warmest spots in product (3 samples from different trays on the rack)	If >5°C at 3 hours then check chiller and air circulation. If >5°C after 4 hours then dispose of product	Temperature checks
	Contamination by airborne contaminants	Scheduled cleaning	Y	N	Y	N	Yes	Cleaning schedule adhered to	Visual inspection. ATP hygiene assessments	Reclean and retraining	Cleaning records and ATP results

Sub-Recipe
Walnut and Wild Mushroom Sauce

Process step	Hazards	Control measures	CCP question 1	2	3	4	CCP	Critical limit	Monitoring procedures	Corrective action	Record
4 Receipt of chopped walnuts	Presence of vegetative pathogens (e.g. *Salmonella*)	Supplier Quality Assurance See Prerequisite Programme (cooking at Step 27)									
	Presence of shells in nuts	Supplier Quality Assurance	Y	N	Y	N	Yes	Greater than specified amount of debris including shell	Intake testing, certificate of analysis	Reject batch if > specification	Intake results and certificate of analysis
	Presence of mycotoxins	Supplier Quality Assurance	Y	N	Y	N	Yes	<2ppb Aflatoxin b1 <4ppb total Aflatoxin	Intake testing, certificate of analysis	Reject batch if >GL	Intake results and certificate of analysis
5 Receipt of dried wild mushrooms	Presence of toxic varieties	Supplier Quality Assurance	Y	N	Y	N	Yes	No poisonous varieties	Certificate of analysis	Reject load	Certificates of analysis
	Presence of heavy metals	Supplier Quality Assurance	Y	N	Y	N	Yes	Must not exceed MRL	Certificate of analysis	Reject if incomplete or no certificate of analysis received or if >MRL reported	Certificates of analysis

Table 1 Example 1: HACCP Chart for Chicken Stuffed with Prawns and Garlic in a Wild Mushroom and Walnut Sauce (Continued)

Process step	Hazards	Control measures	CCP question 1 2 3 4	CCP	Critical limit	Monitoring procedures	Corrective action	Record
6 & 7 Receipt of milk and cream	Presence of vegetative pathogens due to inadequate supplier pasteurisation	Supplier Quality Assurance See Prerequisite Programme (cooking at Step 27)						
	Growth of spore forming pathogens due to inadequate chill conditions	Specification with supplier	Y N Y N	Yes	Limit: 8°C on receipt (product) Target: <5°C on receipt (product)	Product temperature check	If >5°C, but <8°C then check temperature record on tanker filling. If fill temperature <5°C then accept. If >8°C then reject	Temperature checks
16 & 17 Storage of milk and cream	Growth of toxigenic bacteria if temperature not controlled (e.g. *S. aureus*, *B. cereus*, *Cl. perfringens*)	Control of chiller temperature	Y N Y N	Yes	Limit: 8°C Target: 2°C	Continuous monitoring of chiller temperature	If >8°C repair/adjust. If <8°C not achieved within 2 hours then move product to other chiller. If products >8°C reject	Temperature records Process deviations Corrective action and rechecks
8 Receipt of flour	Presence of vegetative pathogens (e.g. *Salmonella*)	Supplier Quality Assurance See Prerequisite Programme (cooking at Step 27)						
	Presence of mycotoxins	Specification with supplier Supplier Quality Assurance See Prerequisite Programme	Y N Y N	Yes	Certificate of analysis with each delivery, compliance with legal limits	Check certificates of analysis	Reject if incomplete or no certificate of analysis received or if >legal limit	Certificate of analysis
	Presence of foreign bodies e.g. stones	Supplier Quality Assurance See Prerequisite Programme (sieve at Step 21)						
9 Receipt of pepper	Presence of vegetative pathogens (e.g. *Salmonella*)	Supplier Quality Assurance See Prerequisite Programme (cooking at Step 27)	Y N Y Y	No				
	Presence of foreign bodies (e.g. stones, insects)	Supplier Quality Assurance See Prerequisite Programme (sieve at Step 22)						
10 & 20 Receipt and storage of salt	No hazards identified							
21 & 22 Sieve flour, salt and pepper	Presence of foreign bodies, stones etc due to incorrect sieve or broken sieve	Sieve	Y Y	Yes	Use of correct sieve No damage to sieve Mesh size 0.5mm	Visual inspection of sieve integrity at 30 minute intervals	If any damage detected then re-sieve affected batch Replace sieve	Sieve checks and replacement

Table 1 Example 1: HACCP Chart for Chicken Stuffed with Prawns and Garlic in a Wild Mushroom and Walnut Sauce (Continued)

Process step	Hazards	Control measures	CCP question 1 2 3 4	CCP	Critical limit	Monitoring procedures	Corrective action	Record
25 & 27 Mix and boil cream, milk, flour, salt, pepper, in hopper, add walnuts and wild mushrooms	Survival of vegetative pathogens (e.g. *Campylobacter*, *Salmonella*)	Cooking	Y Y	Yes	Limit: 80°C Target >95°C	Temperature probing of cooked product	If temperature <95°C then cook for longer until >95°C achieved	Temperature checks
31 Pump sauce from low risk to high risk area	Cross contamination in line or in receiving vessel	Scheduled cleaning	Y N Y N	Yes	Cleaning schedules adhered to	Visual inspection, ATP hygiene assessments	Reclean and retraining	Cleaning records and ATP results
Sub-Recipe **Assembly of finished product (high risk area)**								
35 Place cooked chicken breast in container and place on line	Contamination by environmental/contaminants (e.g. *Listeria*, *S. aureus*)	Scheduled cleaning / Barrier hygiene	Y N Y N	Yes	Cleaning schedules adhered to / Barrier hygiene rules must be followed	Visual inspection, ATP hygiene assessments / Visual inspection	Reclean and retraining / Retraining. Re-entry using barrier rules	Cleaning records and ATP results / Training records
36 Deposit hot sauce onto chicken breast	Growth of surviving spore forming, toxigenic bacteria due to extended holding of sauce prior to fill	Temperature and time control	Y N Y N	Yes	Limit: 63°C Target: Product temperature >70°C on fill	Temperature check of sauce prior to fill	If >65°C then OK. If <65°C but >63°C then all sauce must be filled within 2 hours. If <63°C then dispose of sauce, reclean hopper	Temperature checks Process deviations
37 Heat seal film to pack (and insert into preprinted pack)	Presence of pathogens on packaging	Supplier specification Supplier quality assurance See Prerequisite Programme						
	Pack instructions: Missing date code and ingredient label re: storage instructions and nut allergen	Presence of date coding, storage instructions and walnuts listed in ingredients	Y N Y N	Yes	Correct pack instructions	Visual inspection	If incorrect replace with correct pack instructions	Product labels

Table 1 Example 1: HACCP Chart for Chicken Stuffed with Prawns and Garlic in a Wild Mushroom and Walnut Sauce (Continued)

Process step	Hazards	Control measures	CCP question 1 2 3 4	CCP	Critical limit	Monitoring procedures	Corrective action	Record
38 Metal detect	Failure to detect and/or reject metal in finished product due to machine malfunction	Metal detection Planned maintenance See Prerequisite Programme	Y Y	Yes	Must detect Limit: 2.5mm Fe, 3.0mm non Fe (sphere diameters)(limit of detectability) Target: Absence of metal in finished product	Hourly test of detector using standard detector pieces	If failure to detect test piece then reset detector sensitivity and recheck previous hour's production	Test results
39 Blast chill	Growth of toxigenic bacteria if temperature not controlled	Blast chill	Y Y	Yes	Limit: <5°C, 4 hours Target: <5°C, 3 hours	Temperature probe of product (3 samples from different trays on the rack)	If >5°C at 3 hours then check chiller and air circulation. If >5°C after 4 hours then dispose of product.	Temperature checks
40 Store in chiller & prior to despatch 41	Growth of toxigenic bacteria if temperature not controlled	Temperature control of chiller	Y N Y N	Yes	Limit: 8°C Target: 2°C	Continuous monitoring of chiller temperature	If >8°C repair/adjust If <8°C not achieved within 2 hours then move product to other chiller. If product >8°C reject	Temperature checks

Notes: The presence of nut traces following the production of this product needs to be considered in a HACCP for any product using the same production line

MRL   = maximum residue level
GL   = guidance value

EXAMPLE 2: FOOD SERVICE OPERATION

This example is used to illustrate a simple approach of the application of the principles of HACCP to activities in an operation and is less specific than the approach to an individual product/process. Two activities have been selected for illustration. This approach is particularly suitable for small businesses, including catering, as described in the Department of Health's "Assured Safe Catering" 1993, but may also be applicable to larger businesses where the same operation is used for a wide variety of products.

Terms of reference: Food safety hazards (microbiological and physical agents) from raw materials and ingredients through preparation and handling to service to the customer/consumer. Hazards from chemical agents were considered separately.

Team/skills: Catering manager (proprietor with food technology, hygiene and management skills)
Chef (food hygiene and cooking skills)
Kitchen assistant (food hygiene, cooking and food service skills)

Product: A wide range of dishes to be served in a busy restaurant during a lunchtime period of 1-2 hours.
Products include cold dishes (e.g. salads), prepared desserts, cooked meals served immediately (e.g. omelettes), cooked meals held hot until served (e.g. stew, vegetables) or prepared meals, held at chill temperatures then reheated prior to serving (e.g. microwaveable meals).

Hazard analysis: Each activity was considered in turn in relation to the potential for microbiological and physical hazards to be present or the potential for contamination by these hazards. Professional judgement was used to determine critical points in the operation. Where no subsequent activity could eliminate the identified hazards, the means by which these hazards could be controlled was listed as was the monitoring action to demonstrate that the controls were working. Corrective actions were specified when monitoring indicated a loss of control.

e.g. RECEIPT   The following were included for consideration: fitness of the raw materials/ingredients; the time delay between delivery and transfer into storage; the temperature of the food ingredients at delivery (chilled and frozen materials); condition of the outer packaging; potential for contamination from people; presence/absence of pests.

e.g. COOKING

The following were included for consideration: the potential for the incorrect process to be given (time and temperature settings for a specified size); human error; processing failure.

A record of the hazard analysis is shown in Table 2 for receipt and cooking. Other activities to be considered will include: storage, preservation, chill, hot hold, reheat and service as shown in Figure 4.

Verification

The catering manager checked the records daily and observed the operations at least once per week. All staff were trained by the catering manager and retraining/refresher sessions were held six monthly or as required. Records of training were completed by the trainer and trainee. Planned visits were conducted by the local authority, the findings of which were communicated to all staff, and amendments were made to the food safety system as appropriate.

Figure 7

Example 2 Food Service Operation

Flow diagram: following observation during normal use, the operation was divided into the following key activities (and minor activities which occurred at each step noted for consideration when hazards were to be identified)

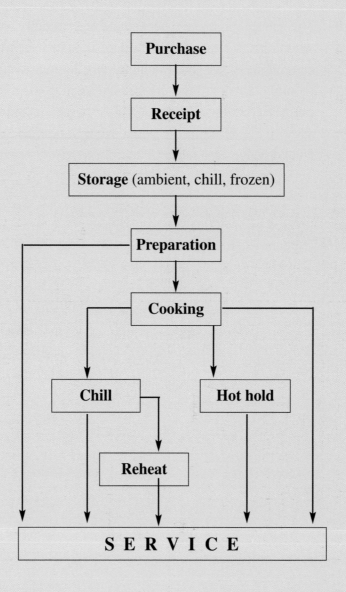

Table 2 Example 2: Food Service Operation

Activity	Hazard	Control	Monitoring	Corrective action
RECEIPT (includes removing outer wrappers and decanting into storage containers, where appropriate)	Contamination of materials due to intrinsic biological or physical agents	Purchase from reputable suppliers	Check condition on receipt (temp; code; appearance) and record	Change supplier
	Contamination of materials with biological or physical agents during unwrapping due to poor handling	Trained personnel / Personnel hygiene policy	Visual check / Visual check	Retrain / Retrain
	Contamination of materials with biological or physical agents during decanting due to unclean containers	Cleaning policy / Trained personnel	Visual check / Visual check	Retrain / Retrain
COOKING	Survival of biological agents due to inadequate cooking	Adequate cooking (to a centre temperature of 75°)	Temperature check and record	Recook or destroy food if recooking would result in a poor quality product
		Trained personnel	Visual check	Retrain

EXAMPLE 3: BAKED BEANS IN TOMATO SAUCE

This example is used to illustrate the large number of control measures that may be required for the control of just one hazard, survival of *Clostridium botulinum* spores. Any spores surviving the sterilization process step could grow and produce toxin in the product, which has a two-year ambient shelf-life. A full study was carried out for product safety from raw material receipt to product despatch and six process steps (Nos. 5, 9, 10, 13, 14, 15) were identified as CCPs. For the purpose of this example only the results for one CCP are shown in detail. Verification procedures are not shown.

Description of Product

The product consists of navy beans in a tomato sauce packaged in a two-piece metal can with a best before date 24 months from the date of production. It is classified as a low acid product and its pH is circa 5.2. It is commercially sterilised, in this example, by a reel and spiral cooker/cooler. In this type of steriliser, movement of the headspace bubble through the can contents increases the rate of heat transfer. A summary of the process flow diagram is shown in Figure 5.

HACCP Analysis

The HACCP team findings for one of the CCPs (Process Step 13) are shown in Table 3 (on pages 56-57). The "process sheet" referred to is the master document giving a full specification of the product and process. The other CCPs are not included in this example. The can and can end were considered in a separate study.

N.B. The list of causes for the hazard are for illustration only and may be incomplete.

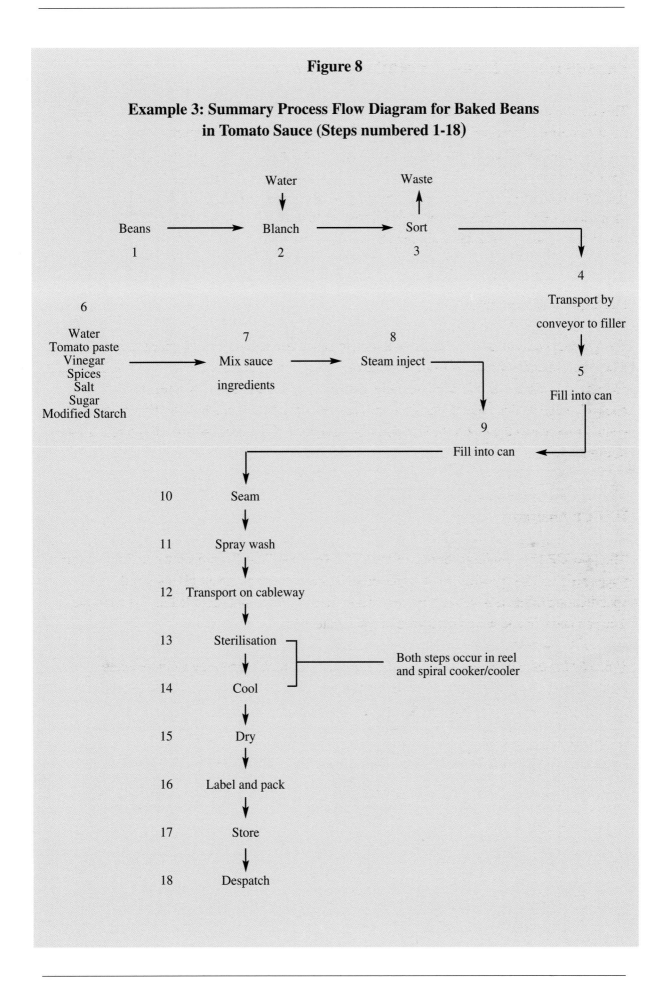

Figure 8

**Example 3: Summary Process Flow Diagram for Baked Beans
in Tomato Sauce (Steps numbered 1-18)**

Table 3   Example 3: HACCP Chart for the Sterilisation Step for Baked Beans in Tomato Sauce

Process step	Hazards	Control measures	CCP question 1 2 3 4	CCP	Critical limit	Monitoring procedures	Corrective action
13. Sterilisation by continuous reel and spiral cooker/cooler	Survival of spores of *Clostridium botulinum* due to poor heat penetration through one or a combination of causes 13.1 to 13.5	* Scheduled sterilisation process based on a "Brimfull" or guaranteed headspace basis, with a minimum initial temperature	Y Y	Yes	Process value must always exceed $F_0 = 3$ so target is set above this	As per process confirmation procedures done annually by Process Establishment Group	*NB. If there is any doubt regarding the adequacy of process given during any production run:* - Quarantine product - Consult Company Microbiologist and Process Establishment Group who will consider disposal options and any process amendments
	13.1 Insufficient headspace - too many beans	* Fill to limits as specified in process sheet			Fill to X ± 4g	As per check weighing procedure by line operator	Reset filler parameters and reweigh
	- too much sauce	* Fill to limits as specified in process sheet. Headspace guarantee device(s)			Fill to Y ± 4g	Use of in-line check-weighers. Supervisor checks records hourly	Recalibrate using cans of known weight
	13.2 Low initial temperature of product at steriliser						
	- filling temperature too low and/or	* Steam injection temperature 95-102°C			Fill at 70°C minimum	Continuous readout and alarm if <70°C. Operator checks readout hourly and when alarm sounds	Operator to consult Sterilising Controller for increased process to be given
	- holding time prior to sterilising too long	* Restrict holding time to the maximum as specified in process sheet			30 minutes maximum holding time	Operator to monitor and record downtime	If 30 minutes exceeded, contact Sterilising Controller for advice on increased process

Table 3 Example 3: HACCP Chart for the Sterilisation Step for Baked Beans in Tomato Sauce (continued)

Process step	Hazards	Control measures	CCP question 1 2 3 4	Critical limit	Monitoring procedures	Corrective action
13. Sterilisation by continuous reel and spiral cooker/cooler (continued)	13.3 Product too viscous - too much starch	* Correctly pre-set the weighing equipment		± 3%	Alarmed weighing system. Supervisor checks records of each product batch	Quarantine and determine extent of excess
	- wrong type of starch used	* Certificates of Conformance for: - delivery - correct storage allocation		Only starches of equivalent type to be used	Product appearance check at batching stage by supervisor and hourly production tastings by QA	Quarantine and determine extent of effect. Process Establishment Group to simulate suspect process by heat penetration tests and determine product safety
	13.4 Steriliser temperature too low - set wrongly	* Set controls as per process sheet		X +1/ -0.5°C	Continuous Platinum Resistance Thermometer readouts and alarms Operator checks mercury in glass thermometer once every half hour	Quarantine. Consult Process Establishment Group to assess safety of product
	- poor heat distribution in cooker shells	* Permanently open steam-shell and condense bleed		Steam free-flowing from bleeds	Operator checks every half hour that steam is flowing from bleeds	Quarantine goods. Inform Process Establishment Group and Engineers
	13.5 Process time too short - software malfunction in cooker shells	* Start up procedure as per process sheet and manual speed check		X ± 1 minute	Supervisor checks rpm of cooker/cooler at least once per shift	Quarantine batch. Consult Process Establishment Group to assess safety
	- misreading of instruments	* Education and training		Accurate reading	Supervisor checks records, once per shift	Quarantine batch and consult Process Establishment Group to assess safety of product. Education and training update

SECTION 5: REFERENCES

British Standards Institution (2000). Quality management systems - Requirements - BS EN ISO 9001: 2000.

British Standards Institution (2001). Guidelines on the application of ISO 9001: 2000 for the food and drink industry. BS ISO 15161:2001.

Campden & Chorleywood Food Research Association (2000) An Introduction to the Practice of Microbiological Risk Assessment for Food Industry Applications. Guideline No. 28.

Codex Alimentarius Commission (1994). Agreement on the Application of Sanitary and Phytosanitary Measures MTN/FA II-A1A-4, CX 11/1 GATT; CL 1994/3-GEN.

Codex Alimentarius Commission (1999). Principles and guidelines for the conduct of microbiological risk assessment. CAC/GL-30.

Codex Alimentarius Commission (2001). Food Hygiene Basic Texts (Second Edition).

Council Directive 93/43/EEC of 14 June 1993 on the Hygiene of Foodstuffs. Official Journal of the European Communities, No. L175/1-11.

Department of Health (1993). Assured Safe Catering. HMSO, London.

Food and Drug Administration USA (1973). Thermally processed low-acid foods packed in hermetically sealed containers GMP (Section 113:40). Federal Register 38, No. 16, 24 January 1973, 2398-2410.

Food Safety Act (1990). HMSO, London.

HACCP Training Standard Steering Group (1995) HACCP Principles and their Application in Food Safety (Introductory Level) Training Standard. RIPH, London.

HACCP Training Standard Steering Group (1998) HACCP Principles and their Application in Food Safety (Advanced Level) Training Standard. RIPH, London.

ILSI Europe (1997). A Simple Guide to Understanding and Applying the Hazard Analysis Critical Control Point Concept. ILSI Press. (Second Edition).

ILSI Europe (1998). Food Safety Management Tools. ILSI Press.

ILSI Europe (1999). Validation and Verification of HACCP. ILSI Press.

International Commission on Microbiological Specifications for Foods (ICMSF) (1988). Application of the hazard analysis critical control point (HACCP) system to ensure microbiological safety and quality. Microorganisms in Foods 4, Blackwell Scientific, Oxford.

Mayes, T. and Mortimore, S. (2001). Making the Most of HACCP, Learning from Others' Experience. Woodhead Publishing Limited, Cambridge.

Mortimore, S. and Wallace, C. (1998). HACCP: A Practical Approach. Kluwer Academic/Plenum Publishers.

National Advisory Committee on Microbiological Criteria for Foods (1992). Hazard Analysis and Critical Control Point System (adopted March 20, 1992). International Journal of Food Microbiology **16**, 1-23.

National Advisory Committee on Microbiological Criteria for Foods (1997). Hazard Analysis and Critical Control Point Principles and Application Guidelines (adopted August 14, 1997).

Owen-Griffiths, A. (2001) HACCP works. Integrated Food Safety Management for Food Businesses. Highfield Publications, Doncaster.

Panisello, P. and Quantick, P. (2000) HACCP and Its Instruments - A Manager's Guide. Chandos Publishing, Oxford.

The Pennington Group report on the circumstances leading to the 1996 outbreak of infection with E.coli O157 in Central Scotland, the implications for food safety and the lessons to be learned. The Stationery Office Ltd, Edinburgh.

Report of the Committee on the Microbiological Safety of Food (Chairman - Sir Mark Richmond) (1990). The Microbiological Safety of Food Part I, HMSO, London.

Report of the Committee on the Microbiological Safety of Food (Chairman - Sir Mark Richmond) (1991). The Microbiological Safety of Food Part II, HMSO, London.

World Health Organisation (1995). Hazard Analysis Critical Control Point System, Concept and Application. Report of a WHO Consultation with the participation of FAO 29-31 May 1995. WHO/FNU/FOS/95.7.

World Health Organisation (1996). Training aspects of the hazard analysis critical control point system (HACCP). Report of a WHO workshop on training in HACCP with the participation of FAO. Geneva, 1-2 June 1995. WHO/FNU/FOS/96.3.

- 60 -